What Do You See?

Written by Judy Nayer ▪ Illustrated by Krystyna Stasiak

MODERN CURRICULUM PRESS

PROJECT DIRECTOR: **Judith E. Nayer**
ART DIRECTOR: **Lisa Lopez**

Published by Modern Curriculum Press

 Modern Curriculum Press, Inc.
A division of Simon & Schuster
13900 Prospect Road, Cleveland, Ohio 44136

ISBN 0-8136-1080-X (STY PK)   ISBN 0-8136-1077-X (BK)

10 9 8 7 6 5 4 3 2   95 94 93 92

**What do you see
when you peek
through the trees?**

3

I see a **beetle**
eating a leaf.

4

What do you see
when you peek
through the trees?

I see a beaver leaving the creek.

What do you see
when you peek
through the trees?

I see a parakeet
cleaning its beak.

8

What do you see when you peek through the trees?

9

I see a monkey
screeching with glee.

What do you see when you peek through the trees?

11

I see a peacock sneaking through the weeds.

**What do you see
when you peek
through the trees?**

13

I see a cheetah
leaping with ease.*

14

What do you see
when you peek
through the trees?

I see
lots of
creatures
peeking
at me!

16